LUMMOX
AND THE FEAST OF THANKS

WRITTEN BY TRACI VANDERBUSH
ILLUSTRATED BY BILL VANDERBUSH

T. ANN PUBLISHING
COPYRIGHT 2019

WHAT IS A LUMMOX?

LUMMOX IS A NOUN OF BRITISH ORIGIN THAT SIMPLY MEANS A PERSON PRONE TO BE CLUMSY.

EVERY PERSON CAN HAVE THEIR LUMMOX MOMENTS IN LIFE. BUT THOSE MOMENTS NEVER EVER CHANGE OUR VALUE OR WORTH.

IN OUR STORIES, LUMMOX IS A LOVING CHARACTER WHO DOES HIS BEST TO BE KIND AND RESPECTFUL TO ALL. SOMETIMES EVEN WHEN WE HAVE THE BEST OF INTENTIONS, THINGS JUST GO WRONG. WE ALL HAVE THOSE MOMENTS.

WHATEVER DAMAGE WE CAUSE OR WHATEVER WE BREAK IN OUR MOST LUMMOXISH MOMENTS, GOD CAN HELP US TO DO OUR BEST TO FIX AND REPAIR AND MAKE RIGHT AGAIN.

IN EVERYTHING, WE DO OUR BEST TO LOVE EVERYONE, JUST AS GOD LOVES US.

HE CLIMBED TO THE ATTIC,
BEING DRAMATIC.
"HEAR ME SAY,
THIS IS THE DAY."

3

"I'LL BAKE SOME CAKES FOR MY FEAST OF THANKS!"

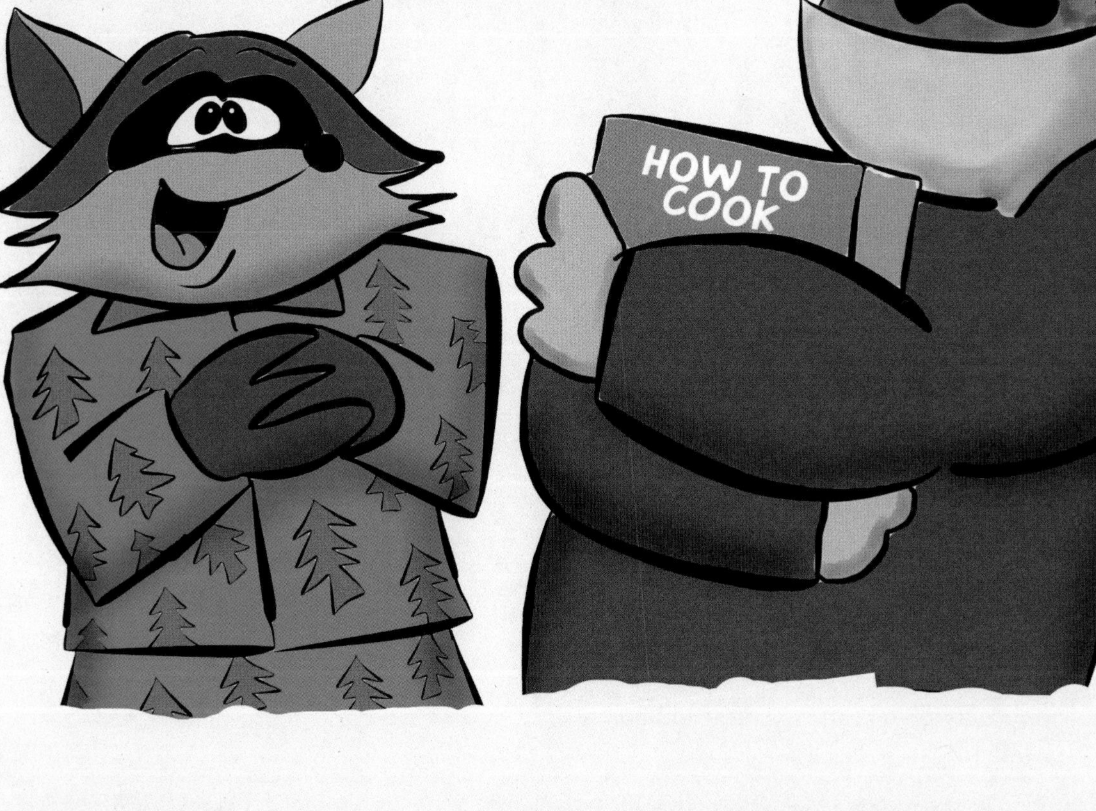

"FRIENDS WILL COME PLAY. IT WILL BE A GREAT DAY!"

6

COON'S EYES WERE WIDE

WITH
JOY
INSIDE

HE WAS
EXCITED!

WHO IS
INVITED?

7

9

LUMMOX SIGHED, "I KNOW HE'S SNIDE. BUT IF WE'RE KIND, HE MIGHT CHANGE HIS MIND.

BEING NICE COULD MELT THE ICE.

FOX IS NOT BAD.

I THINK HE'S JUST SAD."

"MOUSE WILL BE HERE.
HE'S FULL OF CHEER!

HE'LL MAKE FOX HAPPY,
NOT MEAN AND SNAPPY.

FOX WILL BE GLAD
TO MEET SUCH A LAD."

IT WAS TIME TO COOK FROM THE RECIPE BOOK.

EGGS IN FLOUR
AND COCOA POWDER

GRAVY AND MEATS,
AND LOTS OF SWEETS

CORN AND BEANS
BREAD AND GREENS.

SEE MY EYES
ARE THEY THE RIGHT SIZE?

GAMES AND TOYS
AND MANY JOYS

A BALL AND JACKS
CARDS IN STACKS

PUZZLES AND DOLLS

HORSES
IN
STALLS

18

FOX SAID, "HEY MOUSE, WATCH ME MAKE A HOUSE."

LUMMOX SPUN 'ROUND AND FELL TO THE GROUND

21

LUMMOX SHED A TEAR.
"OH DEAR. I'M SORRY,
FOX. I TRIPPED ON THOSE
BLOCKS."

23

BUT FOX WAS RUDE.
"WHATEVER, DUDE!"

IT WAS TIME TO EAT.
THEY SAT IN THEIR SEATS.
TURKEY AND HAM,
PEAS FROM A CAN,
CORN AND DRESSING,
POTATOES AND BLESSINGS.
PUMPKIN PIE,
OKRA THAT'S FRIED.

27

REMEMBER GOD,
REMEMBER GOOD

FRIENDS AND FAMILY,
WE LOVE AS WE SHOULD.

AND TO THE UNKIND,
WE MUST REMIND

GIVE THANKS FOR ALL,
EVEN WHEN THEY FALL.

29

FOX CRIED OUT, WITH A WAVE
AND A SHOUT!
"IT'S NOT FAIR!
WHY SHOULD I CARE?"
HOW CAN I FEAST
NEXT TO THIS
BEAST?"

AWKWARD SILENCE FILLED THE AIR,
MOUSE FELT KIND OF SAD.
PEERING FROM ACROSS THE ROOM
HE ASKED WHY FOX WAS MAD.

"THERE'S A FUR IN MY DRINK, I SMELL A SLIGHT STINK. HIS NOSE MAKES NOISE, AND HE KNOCKED DOWN MY TOYS."

"WE ALL HAVE HEARTS.
WE'RE ALL GOD'S ART.
BIG OR SMALL, SHORT OR TALL
THIN, WIDE, OR SCREWY EYED.
IT'S FUN TO BE
ONE!

FIGHTS MAKE US SAD.
KINDNESS MAKES
US GLAD.

GIVE IT A TRY.
C'MON FURRY
GUY."

35

"IMAGINE LIFE
WITHOUT ANY STRIFE

NO ONE JEALOUS,
ALL ARE SELFLESS.

WE'RE MADE FOR LOVE
NOT PUSH AND SHOVE.

IT'S SO MUCH BETTER
TO WORK TOGETHER

SO LET'S FEAST AND PLAY,
AND HAVE A GREAT DAY!"

37

AS WE WALKED, WE STOPPED TO SEE, LUMMOX TRYING TO CLIMB A TREE.
HE DID HIS BEST, BUT THE TREE BENT DOWN, AND DUMPED DEAR LUMMOX ONTO THE GROUND.

39

BUT DON'T YOU BE
CONCERNED AT ALL

THE AUTUMN LEAVES
THEY BROKE HIS FALL!

"CAN WE BE FRIENDS, AND START AGAIN?"

43

LUMMOX BEAMED.
"YES, WE'RE A TEAM!"

SNOW
WAS EVERYWHERE

46

BACK AT THE HOUSE
WITH COON AND MOUSE
A PEACEFUL SIGHT
A BLESSED NIGHT
SUCH JOY AND FUN
THE DAY WAS DONE

A PERFECT FEAST
FOR A LOVING BEAST.

THE END

OTHER BOOKS BY TRACI VANDERBUSH
(FOUND ON AMAZON.COM AND
TRACIVANDERBUSH.COM)

LIFE WITH LUMMOX
LUMMOX AND THE HAPPY CHRISTMAS
THE PORCHES OF HOLLY
THE WINDOWS OF HOLLY
MR THOMAS AND THE COTTONWOOD TREE
WALKING WITH A SHEPHERD
THE MAGIC OF OUR FOREFATHERS
VIGNETTE: GLIMPSES OF MYSTERIOUS LOVE
SOUL REFORMATION: WHOLENESS FOR THE BODY

WEBSITE: TRACIVANDERBUSH.COM
BILLVANDERBUSH.COM

Made in the USA
Columbia, SC
16 July 2021

41927567R00031